The Earth on Turtle's Back

A Native American Legend

retold by Carol Pugliano-Martin

illustrated by Shirley Beckes

Table of Contents

The Beginning

A long time ago, there was
no Earth. There was only water.
All kinds of animals swam in
the water.

Above the water, there was a place called Skyland. A chief and his wife lived there.

A Great Tree grew in Skyland. Flowers and fruit grew on the tree's branches.

The Dream

One day, the chief's wife told him about a dream she had the night before.

"I dreamed the Great Tree was dug up," she told her husband.

The chief looked sad.

"I am sorry that you had this dream, my wife," said the chief. "Such a powerful dream must be true. Now we must dig up the Great Tree."

The chief dug up the Great Tree. His wife bent down to look at the hole. She lost her balance and fell into the hole.

She tried to stop herself from falling by grabbing onto a branch of the Great Tree. But she was only able to grab a handful of seeds.

The animals in the water below looked up and saw the chief's wife falling toward them. Two swans scooped her up before she hit the water. She rested on one of the swans' backs.

The Plan

"What can we do?" asked one swan.

The other swan looked the woman over and said, "She is not like us. I don't think she can live in the water."

A beaver spoke up. "I have heard that there is earth way down deep in the water. We can dive down and try to bring some earth up for her to stand on."

Several animals wanted to try.
First went Duck. Down, down, down
swam Duck, but he could not reach
the bottom.

Next went Deer. Down, down, down she swam, but she could not reach the bottom. The animals were about to give up.

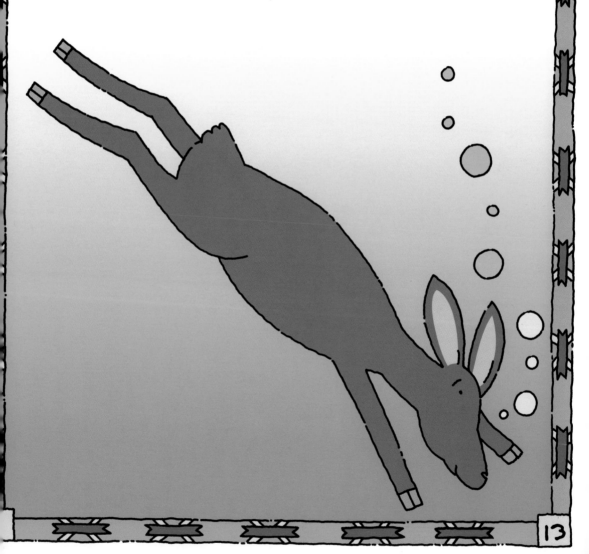

Suddenly, a small voice spoke up. "I will try."

It was a tiny muskrat. The others looked at her with doubt. But Muskrat took a deep breath and down, down, down she swam.

The other animals waited and waited. They were getting nervous.

"She's been down there a long time," said Deer.

"Please, Muskrat. Come back up," said Duck.

A New Life

Suddenly, Muskrat's head popped back up. She held up her tiny paw. In it, she was clutching a bit of earth.

"Hurrah!" shouted the animals.

"Now where can we put this earth?" asked one of the swans.

A deep voice was heard. "Put it on my back."

It was the Great Turtle.

The muskrat placed the bit of earth on the Great Turtle's back. Suddenly, the earth began to grow and grow. It became the world.

The swans placed the woman on the dirt. She thanked the animals and promised to always be kind to them. She opened her hand. The seeds from the Great Tree fell onto the ground.

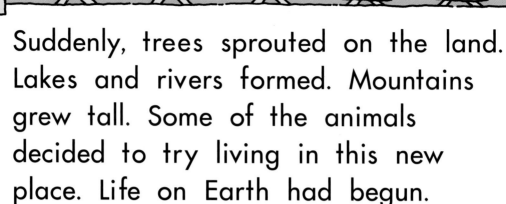

Suddenly, trees sprouted on the land. Lakes and rivers formed. Mountains grew tall. Some of the animals decided to try living in this new place. Life on Earth had begun.